CHARLES LETTS · FOUNDED 1796 · Letts

LEARNING WITH LE

For five- to six-year-old

In Disgrace

Story by Irene Yates
Activities by David Bell, Geoff Leyland,
Mick Seller and Irene Yates

Illustrations by Madeleine Baker

People who live in Cherry Walk

Mum   Dad   Steven   Chris   Harry   Mum   Dad   Beverley
Baby

Jenny   Pusscuss   Kerry   Mark   Charley   Wesley   Rose   Boy

For Jodi

Kerry was upset.

She wanted to watch Mr Johnson feed his birds
in the aviary.
But Dad said she had to go shopping.

'Morning Harry!' Dad called over the fence.

Count the birds in the picture.

How many are eating? How many more would there be on Harry's hand if they all came to eat at once?

Some of the birds are asleep inside the aviary. If Harry has ten birds altogether how many are inside?

Harry didn't answer.

Pusscuss lay on the fence sunning herself.
She squinted at the birds.

Harry squinted at Pusscuss.

What is Pusscuss doing in the picture?
Why is Harry watching the cat?
Look at Harry's face.
Is he happy, sad, cross?
What might Pusscuss be thinking?

Talk about what might happen next.

5

It was so busy in town,
Dad had a job to find a parking space.

Look in the picture for notices
and read them together.

Which tells you who can use this car park?

Look at the sign which tells you when the
supermarket is open. Is it open every day?
When can you go late night shopping?
When does the supermarket close early?

Look at the times. What are you usually
doing at 8 o'clock in the morning?
And at 6 o'clock in the evening?

OPENING HOURS

MONDAY   8am – 6pm
TUESDAY   8am – 6pm
WEDNESDAY 8am – 6pm
THURSDAY 8am – 6pm
FRIDAY   8am – 8pm
SATURDAY 8am – 4pm

SUNDAY CLOSED

Dad pulled the shopping list out of his pocket.
'Now. Let's see what we need.'

'I know what to get without reading a list!' said Mark.

HOME GROWN POTATOES DOWN IN PRICE

20p a lb

Read the signs in the supermarket window together. Talk about what they mean.

Which item costs the most?
Which item costs the least?

What would you choose to buy?
How much does it cost?

Look out for signs like these at your local supermarket.

CHOCO BISCUITS
10p OFF
NOW 30p a packet

ICE CREAM GREAT VALUE
ONLY £1.50

Dad was muttering to himself,
'Spaghetti . . . tomatoes . . . baked beans.'

'Let's get the biggest tin of beans in the world!'
said Kerry helpfully.

How many different sizes of baked bean tins
can you see in the picture?

Where are the smallest tins? Where are the biggest?

Dad wants to buy the biggest and the cheapest
tin of baked beans.
Which colour tin should he buy?

Dad stopped to chat to their next door
neighbour. He gave Kerry and Mark the list
to get some fruit and vegetables.

Kerry is weighing four potatoes on the scales.
How much do they weigh?

How do you weigh food at home?

Find four potatoes and put them on your scales.
How much do they weigh?

Are they heavier than Kerry's potatoes?

Are they lighter than Kerry's potatoes?

Mark loaded the trolley up with ice-cream
while Dad wasn't looking.

Kerry filled up the spaces with chocolate sauce.

Could Dad have known what Kerry and Mark were doing just by listening?

How good a listener are you? Here are two listening games for two players.

1 Player one sits blindfolded while player two makes ten sounds, for example, pouring cereal into a bowl, fastening a zip, winding a clock. How many sounds can player one identify? Now it's player two's turn!

2 Set out six objects on a tray. Study the objects together, then cover them with a tea towel. Player one must now look away while player two places one of the objects in an old shoe box. Can player one identify the object by shaking the box and listening?

'Where did all this ice-cream and chocolate sauce come from?' cried Dad. 'Come here you two!'

Guess how many cartons of ice-cream there are
in the trolley.
Guess how many bottles of chocolate sauce there are.
Now count them. How good were your guesses?

Is the number of ice-cream cartons odd or even?
How do you know if a number is odd or even?

Are these numbers odd or even?
● the number of your house or flat
● your age
● the number in your family.

'Put this stuff back, double quick!' said Dad.
'If you want that lunch at the Pizza Parlour . . .'

'Can I have my favourite pizza Dad?'
asked Kerry. 'Ham and cheese?'

What's your favourite food? What is it you like most about it? Is it the taste? Is it the smell?

Choose a food, such as crisps, that you buy in different flavours. Put the flavours on three or four different plates.

Blindfolded, can you tell which flavour is which by smelling each one? Check each guess in turn.

Now do the test again but this time taste what's on each plate.

Mark chose a sausage and tomato pizza and coleslaw.

Kerry chose a ham and cheese pizza and a raspberry milk shake.

MENU

PIZZAS

HAM AND CHEESE £2.50
SWEETCORN £2.25
SAUSAGE AND TOMATO £2.40

SALADS

GREEN SALAD 80p
COLESLAW 90p
MIXED SALAD £1.00

DRINKS

MILKSHAKES:
RASPBERRY
BANANA OR
CHOCOLATE £1.00
ORANGE JUICE 80p
APPLE JUICE 80p

Use a calculator to work out these sums.

Try to work out how much Mark's lunch cost.
Try to work out how much Kerry's lunch cost.

Which cost more?

What would you choose for lunch? See if you can work out how much it would cost.

Kerry drank half her milk shake.
Dad cut his pizza into quarters.

'This is the way the Italians eat them!'
he said, with a flourish.

How much milk shake does Kerry have left?
How many pieces has Dad cut his pizza into?
How many quarters does he have left on his plate?

Make a sandwich with your favourite filling.
Ask a grown-up to help you cut it in half,
then into quarters.

23

'Great lunch, kids!' said Dad, as they unloaded the car.

Just then Harry Johnson came rushing down the garden. 'It's a good job you're back!' he yelled.

How do you know Harry is upset?
What might have made him angry?

What do you think they bought?
What were some of the things they had
in their shopping trolley?

Do you ever help with the shopping? What do you do?
What do you like best? What do you like least?

Pusscuss was in trouble!

'She's been after my birds!' shouted Harry.
'They're all upset.'

Pusscuss was going mad in the box.
'Mieow! Mieow! Mieow!'

Look carefully at the picture. What things can
you find which are worked by electricity?

Look round your house together. What things can
you find which are worked by electricity?
Notice if the electricity comes from batteries
or from the mains.

Mark said, 'She can't help liking birds!'

'And here's someone who can't help liking cats!' said Dad.

What can you say about the shape of the box that Dad is holding?

Is it a cube, like this?

Is it a cuboid, like this?

How many cube-shaped containers can you find in your home?
How many cuboid-shaped containers can you find?

'Oh, you bad dog!' exclaimed Kerry.

'At least he'll keep that cat away from my birds,' said Harry.

Why does Kerry call Boy a bad dog?
Is Harry still cross?

Try and tell the story to someone – your mum, dad
or a friend – who hasn't read it.

What do you like about the story?
Which part do you like best?
Draw a picture of your favourite part and
write what's happening.

Activity notes

Pages 2–3   Although counting items in a picture is good practice in working with numbers, the best way of helping your child understand simple addition and subtraction is by letting them add or remove objects themselves. It is best if your child does this with the same kind of object, eg if they add apples to apples, or take one brick away from a group of bricks.

Pages 4–5   The questions in this activity ask your child to infer and to predict from what they see in the picture. This involves using visual clues, as well as their own knowledge and experience.

Pages 6–7   At this stage children can relate the things they do to particular times on the clock. For instance, they may know that they usually get up at 8.00 am or have tea at 6.00 pm. Look together at notices about times, timetables, etc, when you are out. This will also help your child's understanding of time.

Pages 8–9   Using words like 'most' and 'least' will help your child begin to understand the value of money. You could put together a collection of items that cost different amounts of money, ranging from expensive to cheap. Talk together about which one probably cost most, and which one cost least.

Pages 10–11   This activity encourages your child to see connections between size and price, and to understand that the biggest item is not always the most expensive. When you are shopping together, talk about the factors that influence your choice of goods, such as size, price, ingredients, packaging.

Pages 12–13   During the first two years of school, children are introduced to standard units of weight such as grams, kilograms, pounds and ounces. Encourage your child to look for these units on the kitchen scales. If they cannot read the numbers, they will be able to see how far the pointer moves along the scale, and to see that one item is heavier than another.

Pages 14–15   Developing our fifth sense – hearing – is often neglected, yet sounds provide important information about our environment. This game encourages real listening concentration.

Pages 16–17   This activity introduces the idea of odd and even numbers. Children may find their own way of remembering odd and even numbers: you could suggest they use a calculator to test whether a number they think is even can be divided by two.

Pages 18–19   Testing separately the smell and taste of a particular food will help your child to understand how closely these two senses work together.

Pages 20–21   Children are now encouraged to use calculators from an early age, but not as a substitute for being able to calculate on paper or in their heads. Using a calculator does enable them to have a go at difficult problems, and they will enjoy playing with a calculator at home. This will help them to find their way around the keys and to learn the importance of pressing the right key.

Pages 22–23   Simple work in fractions begins with children dividing items into halves or quarters. You can help your child make sense of these words by using them whenever you have to divide something like a sandwich or a pie into equal pieces.

Pages 24–25   Talking about your experience of shopping is a way of focusing discussion, as well as involving your child in the story.

Pages 26–27   A simple understanding of the different sources of electricity around the home [including battery and mains] will help children at school when they come to learn how electricity works. Obviously, it's vital to stress how dangerous electricity can be.

Pages 28–29   Distinguishing between two- and three-dimensional shapes is difficult for young children. They often confuse squares with cubes. The more your child can handle flat two-dimensional and three-dimensional shapes, the better. Look together for cubes (difficult to find) and cuboids (much easier) around the house.

Pages 30–31   Encouraging your child to express what they like (or don't like) about a story will help them to build up the confidence to express ideas and responses in other situations, such as classroom discussions.

About the authors and advisers

Irene Yates is a writer and teacher in charge of language development at Lakey Lane School in Birmingham.

David Bell is Assistant Director of Education (Forward Planning) for Newcastle upon Tyne City Council, a former primary head and maths specialist.

Geoff Leyland is Deputy Head of Deer Park Primary School in Derbyshire and a former science and technology advisory teacher.

Mick Seller is Deputy Head of Asterdale Primary School in Derbyshire and a former science and technology advisory teacher.

Elizabeth Bassant is a language advisory teacher in Haringey, London. **Peter Ovens** is Principal Lecturer for Curriculum and Professional Development at Nottingham Polytechnic and a science specialist. **Peter Patilla** is a maths consultant, author and Senior Lecturer in Mathematics Education at Sheffield Polytechnic. **Margaret Williams** is an advisory teacher for maths in Newton Abbott, Devon.